Draw a line from each shovel to the pail of the same color.

Circle the item in each row that is a different color.

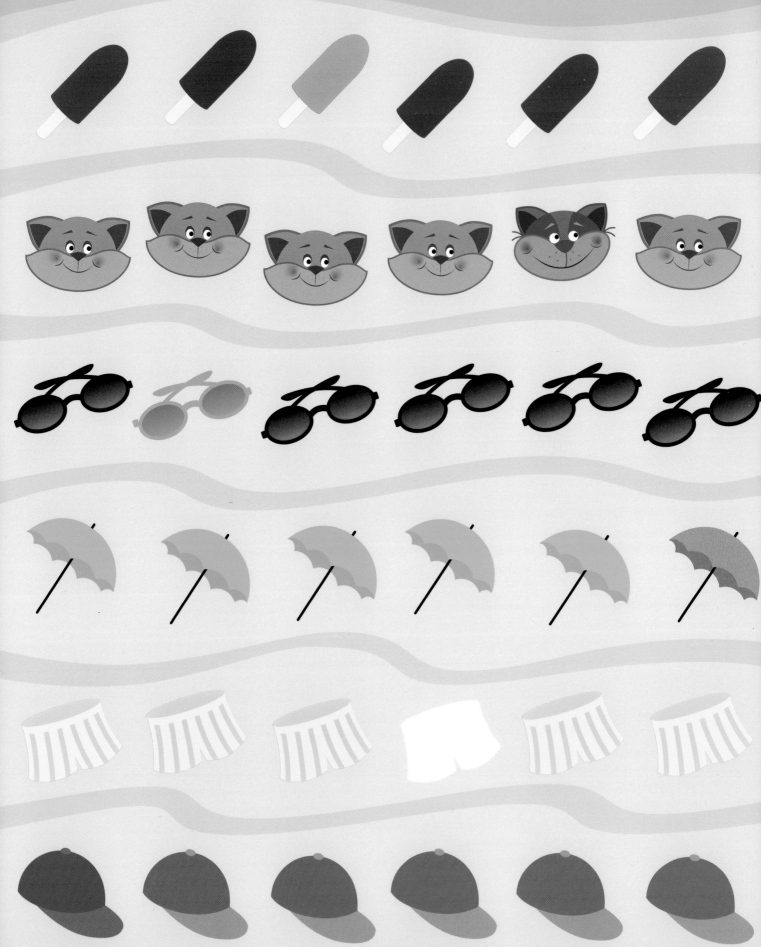

Trace the color word. Then draw a line to match the colored word to the beach chair of the same color. Say the color word.

orange

blue

yellow

green

brown

pink

red

black

purple

5

You can make new colors when you mix two colors together.

Red + Yellow = Orange

Blue + Red = Purple

White + Red = Pink

Yellow + Blue = Green

Black + White = Gray

Gus is going to paint the beach house.
Fill in the blanks and help Gus mix his paints.

Red + _____ = Orange

_____ + Blue = Purple

Red + White = _____

Blue + _____ = Green

_____ + White = Gray

6

Find and circle the color words in the Word Search. Look for these words:

BLACK BLUE **BROWN**
GRAY GREEN ORANGE
PINK **PURPLE** **RED**
WHITE YELLOW

P	B	R	O	W	N	B	W	X	V
Y	U	G	R	A	Y	L	L	G	V
P	E	R	G	R	E	E	N	U	F
R	I	L	P	B	G	H	Q	M	E
Z	E	N	L	L	B	L	A	C	K
G	J	D	K	O	E	X	L	G	U
W	H	I	T	E	W	T	T	A
O	R	A	N	G	E	N	B	L	O

First trace the shape name. Then trace
the shape by starting at the green star
and ending at the red circle.

triangle

square

rectangle

heart

star

diamond

oval

Draw the shape.

heart

square

triangle

Find these shapes in the picture and put a circle around each one.

Draw a line from their fishing bait to the matching fish.

Draw the next shape in each pattern.

Help Gus meet his friends in the water. Follow the footprints and trace the shapes on the path. Then use the same pattern of shapes to fill in the empty boxes.